Tim Hawkins

DISCOVERING JESUS

WHAT IT MEANS TO FOLLOW JESUS

CHRISTIAN EDUCATION
PUBLICATIONS

PO Box A287
Sydney South NSW 1235
Australia
ISBN 978-0-949038-85-2
National Library of Australia

Published 1992. Reprinted 1993, 1994. Revised 1996.
Reprinted 1997, 1998, 1999, 2000, 2001, 2002, 2004, 2010.
Redesigned 2013.
© Tim Hawkins 1992

Typesetting and design: Bethany Abbottsmith
Artwork: Ritchie Priyana
Project manager: Derek Nelson
Managing editor: Natasha Percy

CONTENTS

1

DISCOVERING GOD

TO UNDERSTAND WHY IT'S SO IMPORTANT TO FOLLOW JESUS, FIRST WE NEED TO UNDERSTAND WHAT GOD IS LIKE!

WHAT I THINK ABOUT GOD!

What do you think God is like? What do you know about him already?
Write down some of your ideas here or draw a picture of what God is like.

BE CREATIVE!

 these verses in the Bible, and write down in your own words what they tell you about God.

2 Job 42:2

_____
_____
_____
_____
_____

3 Psalm 147:5

_____
_____
_____
_____
_____

4 Psalm 90:1-2

_____
_____
_____
_____

4

Deuteronomy 33:3

Psalm 5:4-6

_____
_____
_____
_____
_____

_____
_____
_____
_____
_____

7 Tick the box that shows how you honestly feel:

- [ ] I don't think God likes me.
- [ ] God really loves me.
- [ ] God 'puts up' with me.
- [ ] God sort of loves me sometimes.
- [ ] How could God love someone like me?

8 Again, tick the box that shows how you honestly feel:

GOD HATES THE WRONG THINGS I DO [ ]

GOD DOESN'T CARE ABOUT THE WRONG THINGS I DO [ ]

GOD 'PUTS UP' WITH THE WRONG THINGS I DO [ ]

GOD HAS FORGIVEN ABSOLUTELY EVERY WRONG THING I HAVE EVER DONE [ ]

GOD DOESN'T LIKE IT WHEN I SIN, BUT HE KNOWS IT'S NOT MY FAULT [ ]

If I'm really going to start treating God as my king, then here are some of the areas in my life that I'll need to change:

STUDY 2

DISCOVERING ME

WHERE DO I FIT INTO ALL THIS?

WHAT DOES GOD REALLY SAY ABOUT ME?

WHAT THE TV ADS SAY...

1 Lots of people will try and tell you what you should be like.

On the TV screen above, draw a picture of an average teenager and then draw around that person all the products that the ads say the really 'cool' teenager should be using.

2 Genesis 1:26-31

VERSE 27 When God created us, what sort of people did he make us to be?

_____
_____
_____

VERSE 26 Who did God choose to be in charge of everything else that he had made?

_____

VERSE 31 How did God feel after he had made us?

_____
_____

3 Genesis 3:1-16

What happened to change the way that God created things to be?

_____
_____

Romans 1:21
Even though we know God, what important thing do we often refuse to do?

_____

Romans 3:10-12, 23

So how many people in the world are sinning against God?

2 Thessalonians 1:7-9
What will happen to us if we continue to reject God and disobey him?

_____

_____

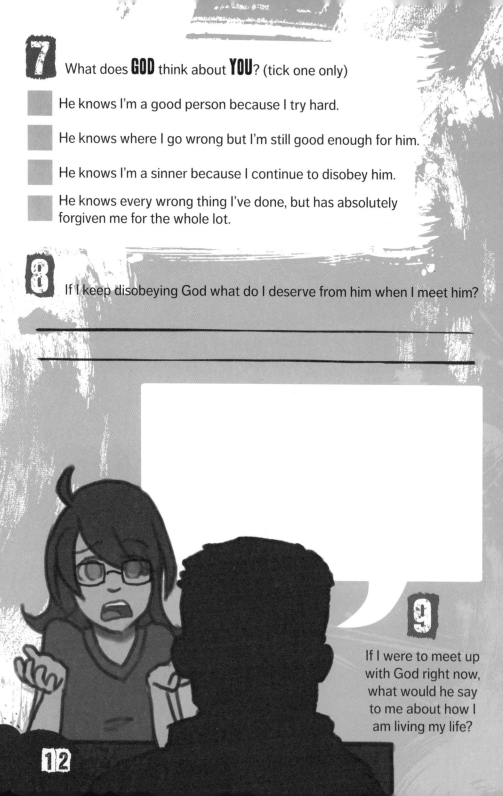

7 What does **GOD** think about **YOU**? (tick one only)

☐ He knows I'm a good person because I try hard.

☐ He knows where I go wrong but I'm still good enough for him.

☐ He knows I'm a sinner because I continue to disobey him.

☐ He knows every wrong thing I've done, but has absolutely forgiven me for the whole lot.

8 If I keep disobeying God what do I deserve from him when I meet him?

_____

_____

9 If I were to meet up with God right now, what would he say to me about how I am living my life?

STUDY 3 DISCOVERING JESUS

> WHO IS THIS GUY WHO HAS CHANGED THE WORLD?

JESUS
IS GOD'S ANSWER TO OUR PROBLEM.

LET'S FIND OUT MORE ABOUT HIM.

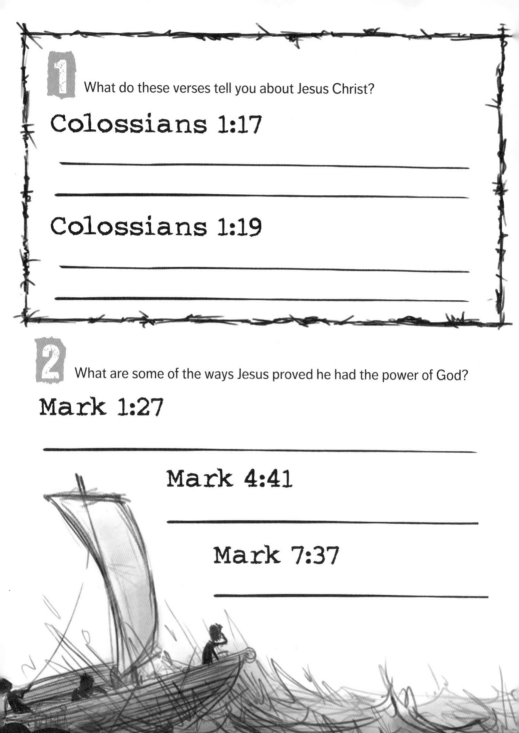

1 What do these verses tell you about Jesus Christ?

Colossians 1:17

_____

_____

Colossians 1:19

_____

_____

2 What are some of the ways Jesus proved he had the power of God?

Mark 1:27

_____

Mark 4:41

_____

Mark 7:37

_____

14

3 Mark 6:34

How did Jesus treat the
people he met?

_____

_____

_____

_____

4 1 Peter 2:22

How was Jesus' life different from
anyone else who has ever lived?

_____

_____

_____

5 This is what I find the hardest to understand about Jesus.

_____

_____

_____

_____

6 These are the qualities in Jesus that I admire the most.

7 This is the way that I think Jesus wants me to treat him.

_____

_____

_____

CHRIST'S LOVE

SO IF GOD IS SO PERFECT, AND I AM SO SINFUL, HOW COULD I EVER LIVE WITH HIM FOREVER IN HEAVEN?

❶
Colossians
2:13-15

VERSE 13
Because of our sins, what sort of state are we described as being in?

_____

What three things has God done for us?

VERSE 13 _____

VERSE 13 _____

VERSE 14 _____

VERSE 15
On the cross, what did Christ do to the devil and the forces of evil (the 'spiritual rulers and authorities')?

_____

_____

_____

2 1 Peter 2:24

What did Jesus carry with him to the cross?

_____

_____

What is the result of this?

_____

_____

3 Isaiah 53:4-6

VERSE 4 Whose suffering did Jesus endure?

_____

_____

VERSE 5 Why was Jesus wounded and beaten?

_____

_____

_____

VERSE 6 Who really deserved Jesus' punishment?

_____

_____

HUNDREDS OF YEARS BEFORE JESUS WAS BORN, THESE WORDS WERE WRITTEN BY ISAIAH ABOUT HIS DEATH.

GOD IS PERFECT
JESUS TAKES ALL MY SIN, SO THAT I CAN NOW LIVE WITH GOD
I AM SEPARATED FROM GOD BY MY SIN
I AM SINFUL

4 Which one of these statements do you believe is correct? (tick one only)

☐ Everyone's sins are forgiven by Jesus' death whether they believe in him or not.

☐ Although Jesus died for everyone, only those who believe in him and trust him are forgiven by his death.

☐ You can only be forgiven by Jesus' death when you always obey God.

5 Tick the answer you think is correct.

The way I can become friends with God is by:

☐ trying to obey him.

☐ going to church.

☐ making up for all the wrong things I've done.

☐ accepting that Jesus has suffered my punishment and asking him to forgive me.

6 So how can you know whether Jesus has really forgiven you or not?

_____

_____

_____

_____

STUDY 5

DISCOVERING MY RESPONSE

SO IF JESUS HAS DONE ALL THAT FOR ME, WHAT SHOULD I DO TO START FOLLOWING HIM?

Matthew 7:13-14

Jesus says there are only two ways that you can live your life.
Let's find out about these two 'roads' you can travel.

	The wide gate	The narrow gate
Where does it lead?		
What sort of road is it?		
How many people travel this road?		

2 Romans 4:25

Why did Jesus die, and
then rise to life again?

_____

_____

_____

_____

3 John 1:12

So what do you have to do if you want to become God's child?

_____

_____

4 Matthew 7:24-27

Jesus describes two house-builders, and says that they
represent two sorts of people. Both of these people hear
God's word, but what's the big difference between them?

_____

_____

_____

5 LOOK BACK AT THE PICTURE OF THE TWO ROADS ON PAGE 23. MARK AN 'X' ON THE SPOT WHERE YOU THINK YOU ARE RIGHT NOW.

6 Take a moment to finish this sentence:

'A Christian is someone who _____

_____

_____

7 How can you know whether you really are a Christian or not?

_____

_____

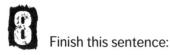 Finish this sentence:

'As a result of what I've learned in these studies, my next step is this:

_____

_____

_____

_____

THE END

26

... or is it

THE BEGINNING?

Now that you've finished **DISCOVERING JESUS**, the next book to help you grow is **FIRST STEPS: STARTING TO FOLLOW JESUS.**

NOTES

PRAYER POINTS

GROWING YOUNG DISCIPLES SERIES

Look for these other great titles in the Growing Young Disciples series

Book 2
FIRST STEPS

Many questions arise in the minds of new Christians. This study book seeks to answer them and reassure young people in their new way of living. They're part of a new family now—one that listens and prays to God.

Book 3
LIFE TO THE MAX

Living our lives as God wants us to. This study book looks at trusting Jesus, overcoming temptation, loving like God does, forgiving like God does and giving like God does. The only way to get the max out of life is to live life God's way.

Book 4
DEALING WITH DOUBT

We all ask questions sometimes about our faith. Has God really forgiven me? Does God really love me? This book gets young Christians looking at the Bible to know for sure the promises and assurance of God.

Book 5
STICKING WITH IT

Sometimes following Jesus can be really difficult! This book spells out the realities of the Christian's walk for new Christians and shows that even when the going gets tough, God loves us and will never desert us.

GROWING YOUNG DISCIPLES LEADER'S GUIDE

This guide covers all five books in the series and contains essential information to help leaders get the absolute best out of kids in junior high, training them to be world-changing disciples of Jesus Christ.

Available from cepstore.com.au